Windows to
Attribute Blocks

REPRODUCIBLE ACTIVITIES
GRADES K-3

**Activities to Develop Logical Thinking
Emphasizing the Most Important NCTM Standards:**

**Problem Solving
Communication
Math Reasoning
Connections**

**By Marilyn Trow and Sue Mogard
Illustrations by Anastasia Mitchell**

This book is dedicated to all the different sizes, shapes, colors, and thicknesses in the world, for it is through explorations of differences that similarities are discovered and appreciated!

seas
AGF 5417

American Teaching Aids • Minneapolis, MN

Editorial Director: Douglas Rife
Editor: Christopher Hartman

©1993 American Teaching Aids • All rights reserved.
Printed in the United States of America

ATA 2888 Attribute Blocks Gr. K-3
ISBN: 0-382-29931-0

This book is concerned first and foremost with connecting to children's needs with the understanding that how children learn affects what they learn. We activated the child within us to move beyond the traditional and obvious activities and uses of math manipulatives. We discovered many marvelous and surprising ways to explore and use manipulatives as learning tools that help children make sense out of many abstract mathematical concepts.

We invite you to enter the world of attribute blocks as adult kids. There is no answer key. The lively style of the book encourages you to become involved as explorers right along with your students. The format supports cooperative learning groups and learning centers, as well as independent exploration. However, we encourage you to always provide opportunities for the children to share their discoveries together in class.

You will find that one exploration leads to another exploration, one question leads to another question, and one discovery leads to yet another discovery.

We can't think of a more exciting way to learn!

Have you ever wondered how some things came to be? Sometimes if you don't know, it's fun to make up stories to explain the origins. Ancient peoples often created stories to explain what they did not understand in their world. The following story is one version of how attribute blocks might have been discovered.

As you make new discoveries about attribute blocks, add new adventures for Gregor and his magical treasures, the attribute blocks. Share the new adventures with a friend. Use a set of attribute blocks to tell the stories!

Once upon a time there lived in ancient Greece a man named Gregor. Gregor loved to entertain the village children with his many games. His favorite game was "Step on the Stone." The streets of his village were made of stones of all shapes, sizes, and colors so Gregor would devise games for the children to play on the stones.

One day the children would have fun trying to step only on the stones that were dark in color while they went to gather wood. The next day the children stepped carefully on the thickest stones while they helped carry items from the market. And another time the children were able to step only on stones that were in the shape of triangles as they played tag in the village square. The children loved Gregor and the games he taught them. One summer Gregor decided it was time for the children to begin creating their own games with stones so he gave each child a set of stones, just the right size to fit in their pockets! Now every child could make up their own games with stones of many shapes, sizes, and colors. The first attribute blocks were created!

Look at a set of attribute blocks. What do you see? Try putting the blocks together in new ways. Find out all you can about a set of attribute blocks:

- Sort the attribute blocks according to shape. Then sort the blocks according to their size.

- Sort the attribute blocks according to color. Is there another way to sort the blocks? Thinking about how the blocks are different may help you find this new way to sort.

- Make patterns with the attribute blocks. How many different patterns can you create?

- Design puzzles with the attribute blocks.

- Share your discoveries about attribute blocks with others.

- Write a short description of each block. Then compare your descriptions with others.

- Arrange several blocks to make a design. Study the placement of the blocks in the design. Then mix up the blocks and try to recreate the design.

- Visualize different shapes to create with attribute blocks.

- Measure items in your world with the attribute blocks.

- See the world in a new way through attribute blocks!

ATA 2888 © 1993 American Teaching Aids • Minneapolis, MN • Made in U.S

You've made lots of discoveries about attribute blocks already!
Completing these sentences will help you recall some of those
discoveries:

I created a

_____

_____ .

(Tell about a design, a pattern, a grouping, and so on.)

When I move this block or add this block the design changes by

_____ .

My favorite design is

_____

_____ .

I think the most interesting fact about attribute blocks is

_____

_____ .

Something new to try with attribute blocks is

_____

_____ .

The attribute block I like best is the

_____ .

Windows to
Shapes

ATA 2888 © 1993 American Teaching Aids • Minneapolis, MN • Made in U.S

SHAPES

Shapes are everywhere you look!

●

Find hidden shapes in your classroom, in the hall, or on the playground.

●

Sit on a chair. What shapes hold you up?

●

Walk through a doorway. What shape did you walk through?

●

Touch your thumb and index finger together. What shape do you see?

●

Make your body into a shape.
What other shapes might you make with your body?

●

Where might you see a triangle in a grocery store?
A square in your bedroom? A rectangle at a park?
A hexagon in your neighborhood? A circle at a toy store?

●

Use your finger to form a shape in the air.
Can you see the shape you drew?

●

Let's get started—get in "shape" with the following activities!

Find the blocks in an attribute block set that have 3 sides. Look closely at the blocks. How many corners do the blocks have?

Triangles are shapes that have 3 sides and 3 corners.

How many triangles are in the attribute block set? _____

What colors are the triangles? _____

_____

Are the triangles the same size?_____

How many different thicknesses of triangles? _____

Triangles come in different colors, sizes, and thicknesses. On this page and the next, trace around and color the different attribute block triangles you have discovered in the spaces provided.

These are the colors of triangles in an attribute block set:

ATA 2888 © 1993 American Teaching Aids • Minneapolis, MN • Made in U.

These are the sizes of triangles in an attribute block set.

These are the thicknesses of triangles in an attribute block set (use a black crayon to show thickness):

2

Find the blocks in an attribute block set that have 4 sides. Look closely at the blocks. How many corners do the blocks have?

Take a closer look at the 4-sided blocks. Are the shapes the same? Find blocks with sides that are all the same length.

A shape that has 4 equal sides and 4 equal corners is a *square*.

Sort out all the squares in the attribute block set.

How many different size squares are there? _____

How many different colors of squares? _____

_____

How many different thicknesses of squares? _____

_____

Squares come in different colors, sizes, and thicknesses. Trace around and color the different attribute block squares you have discovered in the spaces provided below and on the next page.

These are the colors of squares in an attribute block set:

These are the sizes of squares in an attribute block set.

These are the thicknesses of squares in an attribute block set (use a black crayon to show thickness):

You have discovered that a square is a shape with 4 equal sides and 4 equal corners. But there are other 4-sided shapes in an attribute block set. How are these 4-sided shapes different from squares?

These shapes are called *rectangles*.

Rectangles have opposite sides that are equal.
Rectangles have 4 equal corners as well.

How many different sizes of rectangles are in an attribute block set?

_____

How many different thicknesses of rectangles?_____

How many different colors of rectangles? _____

_____

Rectangles come in different colors, sizes, and thicknesses. Trace around and color the different attribute block rectangles you have discovered in the spaces provided below and on the next page.

These are the colors of rectangles in an attribute block set:

ATA 2888 © 1993 American Teaching Aids • Minneapolis, MN • Made in U

These are the sizes of rectangles in an attribute block set.

These are the thicknesses of rectangles in an attribute block set (use a black crayon to show thickness):

4

Find an attribute block that has more than 4 sides. Notice that each side is the same length. How many corners does this shape have?

The block with 6 equal sides and 6 equal corners is called a *hexagon.*

How many different sizes of hexagons are in an attribute set? _____

How many different colors of hexagons are there?_____

_____

How many different thicknesses? _____

Hexagons come in different colors, sizes, and thicknesses. Trace around and color the different attribute block hexagons you have discovered in the spaces provided below and on the next page.

These are the colors of hexagons in an attribute block set:

ATA 2888 © 1993 American Teaching Aids • Minneapolis, MN • Made in U

These are the sizes of hexagons in an attribute block set.

These are the thicknesses of hexagons in an attribute block set (use a black crayon to show thickness):

A 2888 © 1993 American Teaching Aids • Minneapolis, MN • Made in U.S.A.

5

Can you find an attribute block that has no corners? It really has no sides either! This shape is round.

Circles are shapes that have no sides, no corners, and are round.

How many different sizes of circles are in an attribute set? _____

How many different thicknesses of circles? _____

How many different colors of circles?_____

_____

Circles come in different colors, sizes, and thicknesses. Trace around and color the different attribute block circles you have discovered in the spaces provided below and on the next page.

These are the colors of circles in an attribute block set:

ATA 2888 © 1993 American Teaching Aids • Minneapolis, MN • Made in U.S

These are the sizes of circles in an attribute block set:

These are the thicknesses of circles in an attribute block set (use a black crayon to show thickness):

A 2888 © 1993 American Teaching Aids • Minneapolis, MN • Made in U.S.A.

Play a guessing game. Spread a set of attribute blocks on a table.

Describe one of the attribute blocks to a friend without revealing its shape. Challenge your friend to find the block you describe. (Remember to describe the number of sides and corners, the lengths of the sides, the size, color, and the thickness of the attribute block.)

Take turns and invite your friend to describe an attribute block for you to find. Can you find the block in the attribute block set?

Continue until you and your friend have described all of the attribute blocks.

Which descriptions best helped you correctly identify the blocks? Why?

_____

_____

_____

_____

_____

_____

ATA 2888 © 1993 American Teaching Aids • Minneapolis, MN • Made in U.

STAND-UP SHAPES

Some attribute blocks will stand when placed on an edge. Find the shapes that stand on edge. Why do you think these shapes stand and others shapes do not?

Which shape or shapes do not stand?

Make a train of stand-up blocks. Space the blocks close enough together so that each block in the train will touch the next block when knocked over. Lightly tap the first block in the train. What happens? Which shapes work best in the stand-up "domino" train?

Make trains with one or more friends! What's the longest train of stand-up shapes you can make when you work together?

Gather together one block of each shape—one rectangle, one triangle, one square, one circle, and one hexagon. Carry these shapes on a walk in the school neighborhood.

Look carefully at any traffic signs you see on your walk. Do you see signs in the shape of rectangles? What words or pictures do you see on rectangle signs?

Do you see signs in the shape of triangles? What words or pictures do you see on these triangle signs?

Are there signs in the shape of squares? What words or pictures do you see on these square signs?

Do you see any signs in the shape of a hexagon? What words or pictures do you see on these hexagon signs?

Are there signs in the shape of circles? What words or pictures do you see on these circle signs?

When you return to the classroom, complete the next page.

ATA 2888 © 1993 American Teaching Aids • Minneapolis, MN • Made in U.S.

Trace around the attribute blocks you took on your walk around the neighborhood. Add words or pictures to make the shapes look like the signs you saw on your walk.

Create an attribute block playground. Arrange all the different blocks on your desk or table to make fun and exciting playground equipment.

Think of all the possibilities: a thick triangle standing on its edge might be a fast slide, or four squares flat on the ground might make a great four-square, or ...

What other playground ideas can you think of for each shape in a set of attribute blocks? Draw a picture of your exciting Shape Playground on the next page. Share your picture with a friend. Challenge your friend to find all the shapes you used to create your playground.

ATA 2888 © 1993 American Teaching Aids • Minneapolis, MN • Made in U.S.

This is my shape playground. Can you find the shapes I used to create my playground?

"Shape up" with attribute blocks while you get some exercise at the same time! Ready? Try to form your body in a variety of ways to make the different attribute block shapes.

How might you make a triangle with your body?

A circle?

A square?

A rectangle?

A hexagon?

For an added challenge, try making the shapes with another friend or a group of friends. Can you make every shape in an attribute block set using your whole class? Wow!

In the space below, or on another piece of paper, draw a picture of yourself making your favorite attribute block shape.

I am making a _____ .

ATA 2888 © 1993 American Teaching Aids • Minneapolis, MN • Made in U.

Read the story about Gregor on page 5 (or have a friend or your teacher read the story to you). Do you think this story could really happen? Why or why not?

Pretend that you are Gregor. What games might you teach the children to play with the stones of all shapes, sizes, and colors that Gregor brought back in his pocket?

Write your ideas for games in the space below. Then invite a friend to join you in playing your game.

Here are my ideas for some games to play with attribute blocks:

Game #1

_____

_____

_____

Game #2

_____

_____

_____

Game #3

_____

_____

_____

Ask a friend to join you for this activity.

Place a set of attribute blocks on the table. Ask your friend to remove the blocks that have a certain characteristic or attribute. Keep naming attributes until there is only one block left. This isn't as easy as it looks!

Start the game with these directions:

Take away all the attribute blocks that are red.

Take away all the attribute blocks that are thick.

Take away all the attribute blocks that are circles.

Take away all the attribute blocks that have four sides.

And so on!

Take turns. Invite your friend to give you directions for removing attribute blocks!

ATA 2888 © 1993 American Teaching Aids • Minneapolis, MN • Made in U.

Put some attribute blocks in a bag.

Reach into the bag and without looking, find an attribute block. Keep your hand in the bag. Don't look!

Describe the block you are holding.

What size is it?

Does it have corners?

Is it a square? A triangle? A hexagon?

Is it thick? Is it thin?

When you have described the attribute block, remove the block from the bag. Did you guess correctly? Which attribute cannot be predicted by using only your sense of touch?

Continue reaching into the bag and selecting attribute blocks to describe until the bag is empty!

Set the thick attribute blocks on edge in a row on the floor. Leave a space between each block. Which shape is most difficult to put on its edge?

Tape a line of masking tape about three feet (1 m) away from the row of blocks.

Invite two or more friends to bowl with you.

Put one block of each shape represented in the bowling line into a bag. To play, each player in turn reaches into the bag, takes out a block, and then rolls a large marble to try and knock down a matching block of the same shape. Reset any mistakes. Return the removed blocks to the bag each time. Use the score sheet on the next page to record your successful tries.

Are some shapes more difficult to knock over than others? Which ones? Why?

_____

_____

_____

_____

_____

_____

I tried to knock over a _____ .

       I did it. _____   I didn't do it. _____

I tried to knock over a _____ .

       I did it. _____   I didn't do it. _____

I tried to knock over a _____ .

       I did it. _____   I didn't do it. _____

I tried to knock over a _____ .

       I did it. _____   I didn't do it. _____

I tried to knock over a _____ .

       I did it. _____   I didn't do it. _____

I tried to knock over a _____ .

       I did it. _____   I didn't do it. _____

               Final score _____

Trace around each different shape in an attribute block set in the space provided below. Size, color, and thickness do not matter. Trace around any triangle, any square, any rectangle, any circle, and any hexagon.

Gather together all of the small triangles. What attribute block shapes can you make with two triangles? Three triangles? Four triangles? Five triangles? Draw your shapes on the next page.

Gather together all of the small squares. What attribute block shapes can you make with two squares? Three squares? Four squares? Five squares? Draw your shapes on the next page.

Which attribute block shape(s) cannot be created by combining other attribute shapes? Why do you think this is so?

Some attribute blocks, when put together, may be arranged to make other shapes. Here are some examples:

Gather together all of the hexagon blocks to make a set of hexagon blocks. A set is a group of items that share a common trait or attribute.

What sets might you make with attribute blocks that share the attribute of shape, plus ONE other attribute? For example, you might make a set of all the red triangles. This set shares the attributes of shape and color.

Now make a set according to the attribute of shape and TWO other attributes. For example, you might make a set of all of the thick small triangles. These shapes would share the attributes of thickness, size, and shape.

Make a list of all the different sets you discover on the following page. Be creative. Compare your ideas with a friend's ideas. Are there more possible sets?

For an added challenge, make sets according to any attributes you choose. One set may be made up of your favorite attribute blocks. The possibilities are endless!

How many sets do you think you can make using attribute blocks? List your favorite sets on the following page. Ready? Get a set!

ATA 2888 © 1993 American Teaching Aids • Minneapolis, MN • Made in U.S.

Draw pictures of some of your favorite attribute block sets. Beneath each set, write the attributes the blocks in the set share.

Set # 1

_____

Set # 2

_____

Set # 3

_____

Use the back of this page to record more sets!

Create a dot-to-dot attribute block puzzle.

Position an attribute block in the space provided below. Make a dot on the paper at each corner of the block. Lift off the block. Use a ruler to connect the dots.

What shape did you draw? Do all attribute blocks have corners? If not, how might you make a dot-to-dot for a shape that has no corners?

Make dot-to-dot puzzles for other attribute blocks. Set up your puzzles on the next page.

Try making dot-to-dot puzzles with shapes that share one side, or touch in some way (without overlapping).

Exchange your dot-to-dot pictures with a friend. Can you solve your friend's puzzles? Hint: If the dots look all mixed up, position different attribute blocks on the dots to discover the attribute blocks used to create each dot-to-dot puzzle.

ATA 2888 © 1993 American Teaching Aids • Minneapolis, MN • Made in U.S

17

Use this page to make dot-to-dot puzzles. Challenge your friends to solve the puzzles. Can they identify the shapes you used to make each puzzle?

Create an attribute block maze. Make a path of attribute blocks on the floor. Place the blocks at least six inches (15 cm) apart. Try to walk along the path following these directions:

1. Step beside all of the triangles.

2. Step beside all of the rectangles.

3. Step beside all of the hexagons.

4. Step beside all of the circles.

5. Step beside all of the squares.

Add another attribute to the directions and try it again.

1. Step beside all of the red triangles.

2. Step beside all of the thick rectangles...and so on!

Add another attribute to the directions and try it again.

1. Step beside all of the thick, small triangles.

2. Step beside all of the red, large rectangles...and so on!

Is it getting harder? Why or why not? What other directions can you come up with?

For added fun, rearrange the path of attribute blocks and start over.

Windows to
Patterns

ATA 2888 © 1993 American Teaching Aids • Minneapolis, MN • Made in U.S.A.

PATTERNS

Patterns are a part of everyday life.
A pattern repeats a design over and over again.

●

Your clothing may be patterned with stripes or checks.

●

Nature is full of patterns. Look around you!

●

A monarch caterpillar has a pattern on its body.

●

Your flower garden with alternating colors makes a pattern.

●

Waves on the ocean make a pattern.

●

What is the pattern of the colors in a rainbow?

●

What patterns might you see in the hallway at school? At a bakery?

●

Make a pattern of sounds. Make a loud clap and a soft clap.
Repeat it several times.

●

Watch out—pattern finding may become a habit!

A pattern is created when a series of blocks is repeated at least twice. Use the attribute blocks to create exciting and challenging patterns.

Make patterns that repeat a series of different sizes of attribute blocks.

Make patterns that repeat a series of different shapes of attribute blocks.

Make patterns that repeat a series of different colors of attribute blocks.

Make patterns that repeat a series of different thicknesses of attribute blocks.

Once you have repeated a pattern of attribute blocks, ask a friend to continue the pattern.

Record your favorite pattern on the next page.

ATA 2888 © 1993 American Teaching Aids • Minneapolis, MN • Made in U

This is my favorite pattern of attribute blocks. Can you continue the pattern?

Create an attribute block flower. Select a block for the center of the flower. Use other blocks for petals.

Now select a different attribute block for the center of the flower. You might enjoy creating daisies, tulips, violets, or your own variety of flower named just for you! How about a "John-ian" or a "Julie-up?" What might a flower named after you look like?

Share your flowers with a friend. Discuss the patterns the different flower petals create. Put several attribute block flowers together to make a colorful bouquet. (How about making some roses for your teacher?)

Trace your favorite flower on the next page.

                          ATA 2888 © 1993 American Teaching Aids • Minneapolis, MN • Made in U

Draw your favorite attribute block flower here. What is the name of your flower?

My favorite flower is a _____ .

Ready for some 3-dimensional fun? Gather together all of the thick attribute blocks. Stand these blocks on edge. Think about how the shapes might be positioned:

Stand a thick triangle on its long edge or its short edge.

A thick rectangle can stand on any side.

Stand several attribute blocks on edge to create a 3-D pattern. How many 3-D patterns can you make?

For an added challenge, record one of your 3-D patterns on the next page. Trace around the edges of the shapes. Then ask a friend to place attribute blocks on the page so that they match each tracing.

Be careful! This is tough stuff!

ATA 2888 © 1993 American Teaching Aids • Minneapolis, MN • Made in U

Trace a tricky pattern here. Challenge a friend to find the attribute blocks you used to make this pattern.

Place a small attribute block on top of a large attribute block to make a 2-layer design. How many different 2-layer designs can you make? Which is your favorite? A small, thick, yellow hexagon on a large, thin, blue circle is neat! What do you think?

Make a pattern with a series of 2-layer designs.

Look at the pattern you created. What do you like about the pattern? Make a different pattern, and yet another pattern!

Record your favorite 2-layer design pattern on the next page. Trace around the shapes you use in your designs. Color the outlined shapes to match. Make an "X" on the thick attribute blocks in your designs.

ATA 2888 © 1993 American Teaching Aids • Minneapolis, MN • Made in U

Make a 2-layer design pattern here! Why do you like this pattern best?

Every face has a predictable pattern from top to bottom: two eyes, one nose, and then one mouth, in that order.

Create some unusual faces using attribute blocks. Vary the designs of the faces by using different shapes for the features each time you make a new face:

- Layer shapes on top of one another to create fascinating eyes.

- Stand a thick shape on edge to add a new dimension to the faces.

Trace your favorite attribute block face on the next page. Add details to the face, such as eyelashes, eyebrows, lips, and so on if you wish.

Name your face. Add your face picture to a classroom display of attribute block faces. Can you identify which blocks were used to make each face?

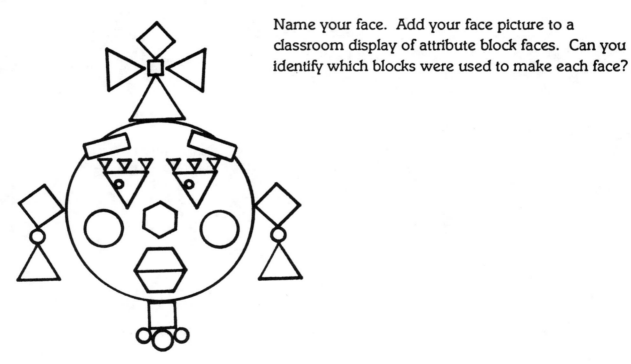

Trace around different attribute blocks to create an interesting face.

Make a pattern using pairs of blocks. First create interesting pairs of attribute blocks. You might stand some thick shapes on edge to make 3-dimensional shape pairs. Repeat a series of the attribute block pairs to make a pairs pattern.

Challenge a friend to use attribute blocks to continue the pattern you create. Can you add attribute block pairs to continue your friend's pattern? Sure you can!

Record your favorite pairs pattern on the next page.

ATA 2888 © 1993 American Teaching Aids • Minneapolis, MN • Made in U.S

This is my favorite pairs pattern. Can you continue the pattern?

25

Invite a friend to join you in playing this game. Divide a set of attribute blocks between you.

1. Player 1 places an attribute block on the table or floor.

2. Player 2 must select an attribute block to place next to that block. It can differ in just one way—thickness, color, shape, or size. For example, if the first block is a small, thick, blue square, the next block might be a small, thin, blue square. The two blocks are different only in thickness. Remember: only one difference for each play.

3. The game continues until a player is unable to add a block to the attribute block train.

Record your favorite one-difference train on the next page.

ATA 2888 © 1993 American Teaching Aids • Minneapolis, MN • Made in U.S

25

Draw a picture of your favorite 1-difference train here. Color each block.
Use a black crayon to outline any thick blocks. Compare your train with a
friend's train. How are they alike? How are they different?

Arrange several attribute blocks together to create an attribute block alphabet! Invite friends to help make all 26 letters.

Is there more than one way to make each letter? Remember, you can stand some attribute blocks on end for added fun!

Which letters are easiest to make with the attribute blocks?

Which letters are the most difficult to make with the attribute blocks?

Make your favorite attribute block letter on the next page.

Use attribute blocks to make your favorite attribute block letter in the space provided below. Trace around the blocks to make an outline of the letter. Then remove the blocks. Now challenge a friend to cover the letter with the correct attribute block shapes.

You can arrange several attribute blocks to form the numbers 1 to 10.

Which numbers look like they would be the most difficult to make? Which numbers look easy to make?

Some numbers have long sections in their shape: 1, 4, and 7. Which attribute block shapes work best for making long sections?

Many numbers have curved sections in their shape: 2, 3, 5, 6, 8, 9, and 0. Which attribute block shapes work best for creating curved sections?

Make your favorite attribute block number on the next page.

58

ATA 2888 © 1993 American Teaching Aids • Minneapolis, MN • Made in U.S

ATTRIBUTE BLOCK NUMBERS

Use attribute blocks to make your favorite attribute block number in the space provided below. Trace around the blocks to make an outline of the number. Then remove the blocks. Now challenge a friend to cover the number with the correct attribute block shapes.

Windows to
Measurement

ATA 2888 © 1993 American Teaching Aids • Minneapolis, MN • Made in U

MEASUREMENT

People use units of measurement to make clothes, package foods, build homes, and design cars. Measurement is used to make everything!

●

Think of all the ways you use measurement.

●

How tall are you?

●

How much do you weigh?

●

How far is it to the grocery store?

●

What size shoes do you wear?

●

How fast does an airplane fly?

●

How big is an atom?

●

Look what you might discover through measuring!

●

How do you "measure up?" Try these activities and find out!

A 2888 © 1993 American Teaching Aids • Minneapolis, MN • Made in U.S.A.

The distance around a shape is its *perimeter*.

Which attribute block do you think has the largest perimeter?

Gather together all of the large attribute block shapes. Predict which shape has the greatest perimeter.

Arrange the blocks in order from largest perimeter to smallest perimeter. Then measure the distance around each attribute block to check your predictions!

How did you measure the distance around the attribute blocks? How did your friends measure their attribute blocks?

Use string to measure items that do not have straight sides. Hold the end of the string at one point on the edge of an attribute block. Gently pull the string all the way around the outside edge of the attribute block back to that point again. Cut the string where you stop measuring. Straighten out the piece of string and you have the perimeter of the attribute block. Compare the lengths of the different strings to determine which shape has the greatest perimeter!

Now gather together all the different small attribute block shapes. Predict which of these shapes has the greatest perimeter. How can your measurement of the large attribute block shapes help you in making your prediction? Measure the perimeters to check your predictions. How did you do?

What items in your classroom have the same perimeters as the attribute blocks? Does an eraser have the same perimeter as a small rectangle? Measure to see! Find other items to measure and match perimeters with the attribute blocks. Record your discoveries on the next two pages by drawing pictures of the items you measured.

ATA 2888 © 1993 American Teaching Aids • Minneapolis, MN • Made in U

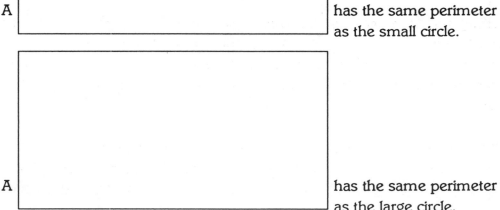

Look at all of the items that have the same perimeters as my attribute blocks!

A [   ] has the same perimeter as the small rectangle.

A [   ] has the same perimeter as the large rectangle.

A [   ] has the same perimeter as the small circle.

A [   ] has the same perimeter as the large circle.

Look at all of the items that have the same perimeters as my attribute blocks!

A ⬜ has the same perimeter as the small square.

A ⬜ has the same perimeter as the large square.

A ⬜ has the same perimeter as the small hexagon.

A ⬜ has the same perimeter as the large hexagon.

ATA 2888 © 1993 American Teaching Aids • Minneapolis, MN • Made in U.

How might you measure items in your classroom using only an attribute block circle? Any ideas? Try using one rotation of the circle as your unit of measure. Use the same rotation for everything you measure and you can compare the measurements of different items.

Put a small piece of masking tape at a point along the edge of one of the large attribute block circles. It can be a thick or thin circle.

Position the circle on its edge. Hold the circle at its center point loosely between your thumb and index finger. Use the circle to measure the length of your desk. Start at one end of the desk. Put the taped part of the circle on the edge of the desk. Now carefully roll the circle across the desk top. Count the number of times the tape touches the desk surface. Each touch represents one full rotation.

Using each rotation as the unit of measurement, measure other items in your classroom. Record your measurements on the next page.

I can measure items using the large circle from an attribute block set.

_____ measures _____ rotations.

_____ measures _____ rotations.

_____ measures _____ rotations.

_____ measures _____ rotations.

_____ measures _____ rotations

_____ measures _____ rotations.

_____ measures _____ rotations.

_____ measures _____ rotations.

_____ measures _____ rotations.

_____ measures _____ rotations.

_____ measures _____ rotations.

_____ measures _____ rotations.

_____ measures _____ rotations.

_____ measures _____ rotations.

_____ measures _____ rotations.

ATA 2888 © 1993 American Teaching Aids • Minneapolis, MN • Made in U.S

Which attribute blocks do you think weigh the most? Weigh the least?
Why? Gather together a balancing scale and several small items to
find out!

Place three attribute blocks on one side of the scale. What items can you
find to add to the other side of the scale to make it balance?

Try putting several large, thick attribute blocks on the scale. What items
can you find to add to the other side of the scale to make it balance?

Put several thin, small attribute blocks in the scale. What items can you
find to add to the other side of the scale to make it balance?

What items balance a thin and a thick attribute block? Does the shape of
the blocks make a difference? Does the size
of the blocks make a difference?

What discoveries did you make? Record the
results on the next page.

WEIGHTY ATTRIBUTE BLOCKS

I weighed these items with attribute blocks. Here's what I found:

A _____
(write the name of the item here)

weighed _____ .
(write the attribute blocks here)

A _____
(write the name of the item here)

weighed _____ .
(write the attribute blocks here)

A _____
(write the name of the item here)

weighed _____ .
(write the attribute blocks here)

A _____
(write the name of the item here)

weighed _____ .
(write the attribute blocks here)

A _____
(write the name of the item here)

weighed _____ .
(write the attribute blocks here)

A _____
(write the name of the item here)

weighed _____ .
(write the attribute blocks here)

ATA 2888 © 1993 American Teaching Aids • Minneapolis, MN • Made in U.S

Select a large square from an attribute block set. Place the square on top of your math book. How many squares do you think it will take to cover the top of your math book? Write your prediction here: _____

Now gather together several large attribute block squares to test your prediction. Was your prediction close?

The number of squares it takes to cover your math book is called its area.

How might you find the area of the top of your desk? If you don't have enough squares to cover the desk, how might you predict its area?

Discover the area of flat surfaces in your classroom using square attribute blocks. Write your results on the next page.

The flat surfaces in my room have attribute block areas!

A _____ has an area of _____ square attribute blocks.
(write the name of item)

A _____ has an area of _____ square attribute blocks.
(write the name of item)

A _____ has an area of _____ square attribute blocks.
(write the name of item)

A _____ has an area of _____ square attribute blocks.
(write the name of item)

A _____ has an area of _____ square attribute blocks.
(write the name of item)

A _____ has an area of _____ square attribute blocks.
(write the name of item)

A _____ has an area of _____ square attribute blocks.
(write the name of item)

A _____ has an area of _____ square attribute blocks.
(write the name of item)

A _____ has an area of _____ square attribute blocks.
(write the name of item)

A _____ has an area of _____ square attribute blocks.
(write the name of item)

A _____ has an area of _____ square attribute blocks.
(write the name of item)

What different size shadows can you make using attribute blocks and a flashlight?

Stand a thick triangle on its edge. Shine the flashlight over the triangle. What shadow does the triangle make?

Move the flashlight from side to side and back and forth. Move the flashlight over the top of the shape and back again. How does the shadow of the triangle change as you move the flashlight?

Try the experiment again with a thick square. How is the square's shadow different from the triangle's shadow? Cast other shadows using other attribute blocks.

Try making long shadows.

How can you make the shadows shorter?

_____

_____

_____

Which attribute block makes the longest shadow?

_____

_____

_____

32

I can make different sized shadows using attribute blocks. Trace around the shadows in the spaces provided below.

This is the longest shadow I can make with a _____ .

(write the name of attribute block)

This is the strangest shadow I can make with a _____ .

(write the name of attribute block)

This is the funniest shadow I can make with a _____ .

(write the name of attribute block)

ATA 2888 © 1993 American Teaching Aids • Minneapolis, MN • Made in U.S

What structures can you build using attribute blocks? Stand the thick blocks on edge for supports. Use the thin blocks as the building surfaces.

How might you make a table? A tower? A box?

Build the tallest structure possible. How did you do it?

Build the strongest structure possible. Which blocks were most useful?

For an added challenge, use all of the attribute blocks to build a structure! What does it look like? Compare your structure to your classmates' structures.

Who has the tallest structure? _____

The widest structure? _____

First decide what you could use to measure the structures. Try to think of something besides a ruler.

I will measure the structures with

_____

The tallest structure measured _____ high.

The widest structure measured _____ wide.

The shortest structure measured _____ high.

The narrowest structure measured _____ wide.

Draw a picture of your favorite attribute block structure on the next page.

33

MEASURE THE STRUCTURE

This is my favorite attribute block structure!

ATA 2888 © 1993 American Teaching Aids • Minneapolis, MN • Made in U.

Windows to Your World

ATTRIBUTE BLOCKS IN YOUR WORLD

Attribute blocks can be used as windows to new thinking in all subject areas.

●

Attribute blocks can be used to write creative stories!

●

Try making an attribute block dinosaur for some BIG fun!

●

Can you create a diorama using attribute blocks?

●

How about designing attribute block masterpieces in art?

●

What other ways might you use attribute blocks in your world?

You will need some modeling clay to create this masterpiece.

Flatten out the modeling clay to create a smooth surface.

Press different attribute blocks into the surface of the clay to make interesting impressions. Try using the edges, corners, and sides of attribute blocks to make the impressions. Notice how the thicker attribute blocks make deeper impressions than the thinner blocks.

When your design is complete, invite a friend to guess which attribute blocks you used to make each impression.

Allow your modeling clay to dry. When dry, paint your design to truly make it a work of art!

ATTRIBUTE BLOCK DIORAMAS

You can make an interesting diorama with attribute blocks. You will need a shoe box, some clay, and a set of attribute blocks to create the diorama.

Arrange several attribute blocks together in the shoe box to create a scene. Which attribute blocks might become clouds? Which attribute blocks might make great mountains? Little bits of clay will secure the blocks in place.

If you wish, add small figurines or other items to the diorama for detail.

Try creating a scene from a book you read. Invite a friend to guess what book you read by looking at your diorama. Be creative!

35

ATA 2888 © 1993 American Teaching Aids • Minneapolis, MN • Made in U.

Assign a value to each attribute block according to its size, shape, and thickness. For example, the large, thick blocks might have the greatest values assigned to them and the small, thin blocks might have lesser values. Record your values for each block in the chart below.

I assigned these values to attribute blocks:

LARGE SQUARE   _____   SMALL SQUARE   _____

LARGE TRIANGLE   _____   SMALL TRIANGLE   _____

LARGE RECTANGLE   _____   SMALL RECTANGLE   _____

LARGE CIRCLE   _____   SMALL CIRCLE   _____

LARGE HEXAGON   _____   SMALL HEXAGON   _____

Put all the attribute blocks in a bag. Reach into the bag and remove several blocks. Find the total value of the blocks. Put the blocks back into the bag. Try it again! Reach into the bag and remove some more blocks. Do these blocks have a greater value?

Try it again! What total did you get?

What is the largest possible total? The smallest possible total? Record the results in the chart on the next page.

2888 © 1993 American Teaching Aids • Minneapolis, MN • Made in U.S.A.

	ATTRIBUTE BLOCKS	VALUE
Handful 1		
Handful 2		
Handful 3		
Handful 4		
Handful 5		
Handful 6		

ATA 2888 © 1993 American Teaching Aids • Minneapolis, MN • Made in U.

Use attribute blocks to design a machine that will do something helpful or extraordinary.

Maybe you will make a futuristic rocket ship to shuttle people to the moon for vacations.

You might wish to make a machine that does homework. That would be an interesting machine to watch!

When you finish designing your machine, explain what each part of your machine does.

The name of my new machine is _____

This machine can _____

_____

_____

This is how it works: _____

_____

_____

_____

_____

_____

Draw a picture of your machine on the next page. Label all the special parts of the machine.

This is my attribute block machine:

ATA 2888 © 1993 American Teaching Aids • Minneapolis, MN • Made in U.S.

Trace around each different large attribute block shape. Use the next page to make your tracings.

Look at the shapes carefully. What words come to mind for the various shapes? Write the words inside each shape.

In which shape might you write the word *bubble*? Why might this word go with this shape?

In which shape might you write the word *house*? Why might this word go with this shape? Is there another shape that might also be described by this word?

In which shape might you write the word *honeycomb*? Why might this word go with this shape?

In which shape might you write the words *candy bar*? Why might these words go with this shape?

In which shape might you write the words *pine tree*? Why might these words go with this shape?

What other words will you write for each attribute block shape?

Share your shape words with a friend. What other ideas does your friend have for each shape?

For added fun, make a group list of the words you and your classmates discover. You could write the words up on the chalkboard for everyone to see.

Trace around each different large attribute block in the space provided below. Inside each shape, write words that the shape brings to mind!

You can use attribute blocks to make interesting prints! Here's how:

Materials
- Tempera paint
- Pie tin
- Paper towels
- Attribute blocks
- Construction paper

Mix your favorite color tempera paint in a pie tin. Place several layers of paper towels in the tin until the towels are completely soaked through with paint.

Press one edge of an attribute block on the paint-saturated paper towels. Press the painted edge on a sheet of construction paper to make a print. Press different edges, sides, or faces (the flat sides) of attribute blocks on the paper towels to make other prints on the paper.

Make an attribute block print design. When your masterpiece is complete, challenge a friend to guess which attribute blocks you used to make each print in your design.

Have you ever seen an attribute block dinosaur? What blocks might be used to make *Tyrannosaurus rex*? *Apatosaurus*?

Think about which attribute blocks might make a strong neck, a long powerful tail, a huge head, pointed spines, and so on.

Create a dinosaur with attribute blocks. Trace the dinosaur on the next page. Invite your classmates to display their attribute block dinosaurs in the classroom. Put your dinosaur picture in the display as well. Do not write the names of the dinosaurs on the papers. Can you identify all of the dinosaurs?

ATTRIBUTE BLOCK DINOSAURS

I can make a dinosaur from attribute blocks. Can you guess which
dinosaur I made?

Design a vehicle using attribute blocks. Which shape will you use for tires?

Can you make a roadster? How might you make a Model T?

What might a van look like? For an added challenge, make a bus or a semi-truck! How many wheels do these vehicles have?

Trace your vehicle on the next page. Then write about a trip you might take in your brand-new vehicle. What exciting adventures await you!

ATA 2888 © 1993 American Teaching Aids • Minneapolis, MN • Made in U.S

This new vehicle is called a _____ !

I can't wait to take a trip to _____ .

While I am there I want to _____

_____ .

Look carefully at the different blocks in a set of attribute blocks. Think about how each block makes you feel.

Which shape might you use to tell about yourself? Do you feel smooth around the edges like a circle, or full of pointed thoughts like a triangle?

Does a thin or thick attribute block express how you feel today? Are you feeling sure of yourself like a thick attribute block, or more quiet like a thin block?

How about the size of your feelings today? Are they very strong and large emotions like a large attribute block? Or do you feel less strong emotions?

Choose the attribute block that best expresses how you feel today. Trace the block on the next page. Explain why the block you selected best expresses you!

To really get to know yourself better, choose an attribute block to express yourself every day for a week. Did you choose the same block each day? Why or why not? What does this tell you about yourself?

ATA 2888 © 1993 American Teaching Aids • Minneapolis, MN • Made in U.

EXPRESS YOURSELF!

This attribute block expresses how I feel today!

I have chosen this attribute block because _____

_____

_____

_____

_____

_____

_____

Place a check mark by the attribute block activity windows you have completed. Put a star by your favorite activities. Tell your teacher or parent about them!

Windows to Shapes

1. Triangles
2. Squares
3. Rectangles
4. Hexagons
5. Circles
6. I'm Thinking of …
7. Stand-up Shapes
8. Shape Signs
9. Shape Playground

10. Shape Up!
11. Gregor's Game
12. "Simon Says"
13. Name that Shape!
14. Attribute Block Bowling
15. Hidden Shapes
16. Ready? Get a *SET!*
17. Dot-to-Dot
18. Follow the Trail

Windows to Patterns

19. Patterns for Everyone
20. Flowers Galore
21. 3-D Patterns
22. Double-Layer Patterns
23. Design a Face

24. Connect Two
25. One-Difference Game
26. Attribute Block Alphabet
27. Attribute Block Numbers

ATA 2888 © 1993 American Teaching Aids • Minneapolis, MN • Made in U

Windows to Measurement

28. Matching Perimeters

29. Round Rulers

30. Weighty Attribute Blocks

31. Attribute Block Areas

32. Shadow Measurements

33. Measure the Structure

Windows to Your World

34. Make an Impression

35. Attribute Block Dioramas

36. Valued Attribute Blocks

37. Make a Machine

38. Shape Words

39. Attribute Block Prints

40. Attribute Block Dinosaurs

41. Attribute Block Vehicles

42. Express Yourself

Congratulations!

BE IT KNOWN THAT

_____

DEMONSTRATING CURIOSITY, CREATIVITY, AND EXCEPTIONAL
PROFICIENCY
IN THE SCIENCE OF ATTRIBUTE BLOCKOLOGY,

HAS COMPLETED

Windows to Attribute Blocks!

_____

Signed

including:
- Windows to Shapes
- Windows to Patterns
- Windows to Measurement
- Windows to Your World

Ready for more mind stretchers? These books encourage creative thinking. Many of them may be explored and enjoyed independently but you'll want to share them with your friends.

Adler, David A., *Base Five*, Crowell, 1975.

Anno, Mitsumasa, *Anno's Mysterious Multiplying Jar*, Philomel Books, 1983.

Anno, Mitsumasa, *Socrates and the Three Little Pigs*, Philomel Books, 1985.

Asimov, Isaac, *Realm of Numbers*, Houghton Mifflin, 1959.

Berman, Paul, *The World of Numbers*, Marshall Cavendish Corp., 1989.

Berry, Marilyn, *Help Is on the Way for: Charts and Graphs*, Children's Press, 1985.

Brittannica Discovery Library, *Numbers Book*, Encyclopedia Britannica, 1974.

Brown, Sam, *One, Two, Buckle My Shoe*, Gryphon House, 1982.

Burns, Marilyn, *Math for Smarty Pants*, Little, Brown and Co., 1982.

Charosh, Mannis, *Number Ideas Through Pictures*, Crowell, 1974.

Dennis, J. Richard, *Fractions Are Parts of Things*, Crowell, 1971.

Fisher, Leonard Everett, *Number Art*, Four Winds Press, 1982.

Freeman, Mae, *Finding Out About Shapes*, McGraw-Hill, 1969.

Froman, Robert, *The Greatest Guessing Game*, Crowell, 1978

Froman, Robert, *Venn Diagrams*, Crowell, 1972.

Gersting, Judith L. and Joseph E. Kuczkowski, *Yes No Stop Go*, Crowell, 1977.

Phillips, Jo, *Right Angles*, Crowell, 1972.

Pluckrose, Henry, *Knowabout Capacity*, Franklin Watts, 1988.

Pluckrose, Henry Arthur, *Knowabout Sorting*, Franklin Watts, 1988.

Schwartz, David M., *How Much Is a Million?*, Lothrop, Lee, and Shepard Books, 1985.

Trivett, John V., *Building Tables on Tables*, Crowell, 1975.

Watson, Clyde, *Binary Numbers*, Crowell, 1977.

Weiss, Malcolm E., *666 Jelly Beans! All That?*, Crowell, 1976.

Weiss, Malcolm E., *Solomon Grundy, Born on Oneday*, Crowell, 1977.